**COMMON
GROUND**
BOOKS

To my Mom, Stephanie, who instilled in me the wonder, joy, and true meaning of Christmas. I continue to carry on her Christmas spirit through the years.

To my children, Emma, Brady, and Samuel, who are represented in this book via the illustrations, characters, and rhymes. May Christmas time always be a joyous and special part of your lives.

To my wife, Jocelyn. Thank you for your love and support and for always believing in my vision.

SCAN ME

This Snowman
(Tune of "This Old Man")

Chorus: With a carrot for a nose and two eyes made out of coal,
this snowman's from the North Pole

This Snowman, he played one, building him is so much fun

This Snowman, he played two, every year he's made anew

This Snowman, he played three, outside time for my friends and me

This Snowman, he played four, he threw snowballs at my door

This Snowman, he played five, the Winter makes him come alive

This Snowman, he played six, his two arms are made of sticks

This Snowman, he played seven, it's dark outside with stars in heaven

This Snowman, he played eight, my Mom yells out "It's getting late"

This Snowman, he played nine, he melted in the warm sunshine

This Snowman, he played ten, I'll build him when it snows again

Sing A Song Of Christmas

(Tune of "Sing A Song Of Sixpence")

Sing a song of Christmas

The best time of the year

A season full of wonder

The season full of cheer

Fill your hearts with kindness

Open up your hearts

Spread love all around you

This is where it starts

Brady, Brady, Cookie Baker

(Tune of "Peter, Peter, Pumpkin Eater")

Brady, Brady, Cookie Baker

Baked some cookies to save for later

He put them in a cookie jar

Those cookies he made, didn't get very far

Brady, Brady, Cookie Baker

Baked some cookies to save for later

He put them in a cookie jar

Those cookies he made, didn't get very far

Little Miss Emma

(Tune of "Little Miss Muffet")

Little Miss Emma

Had a dilemma

She lost her Christmas list

She cried for a while

Then suddenly smiled

It was under the cookie dish

String String String Your Lights

(Tune of "Row Row Row Your Boat")

String string string your lights

All around your tree

Decorate it up and down

It's sure a sight to see

String string string your lights

All around your tree

Decorate it up and down

It's sure a sight to see

Sparkle Sparkle Christmas Tree
(Tune of "Twinkle Twinkle Little Star")

Sparkle sparkle Christmas tree

Shining bright for all to see

Bring us joy at Christmas time

Your beauty makes us shine inside

Sparkle sparkle Christmas tree

Shining bright for all to see

Five Little Elves

(Tune of "Five Little Ducks")

Five little elves made toys one day
To load them up on Santa's sleigh
Santa Claus laughed "Ho Ho Ho Ho"
Only four little elves were ready to go

Four little elves made toys one day
To load them up on Santa's sleigh
Santa Claus laughed "Ho Ho Ho Ho"
Only three little elves were ready to go

Three little elves made toys one day
To load them up on Santa's sleigh
Santa Claus laughed "Ho Ho Ho Ho"
Only two little elves were ready to go

Two little elves made toys one day
To load them up on Santa's sleigh
Santa Claus laughed "Ho Ho Ho Ho"
Only one little elf was ready to go

One little elf made toys one day
To load them up on Santa's sleigh
Santa Claus laughed "Ho Ho Ho Ho"
"Where did all my little elves go?"

All the toys were on the sleigh
To deliver them for Christmas Day
Santa Claus said "It's starting to snow"
And his five little elves were ready to go

Little Man Sam

(Tune of "Little Boy Blue")

Little man Sam, it's time for bed

Santa is coming, you know what he said

Be sure to be asleep

Why is this you say?

So I can drop off your gifts

Before Christmas day

Will I get presents?

Of course, my dear

You have been good all through the year

Ho Ho, Santa
(Tune of "Baa Baa Black Sheep")

Ho ho, Santa

Have you any toys?

Yes kids, yes kids

All the girls and boys

A dolly for Harper

A necklace for Belle

Cole wants a football

And Ava won't tell

Ho ho, Santa

Have you any toys?

Yes kids, yes kids

All the girls and boys

Mary & Joe

(Tune of "Jack and Jill")

Mary and Joe, traveled to and fro

To welcome their new baby boy

An angel came down, to see what was around

Then proclaimed to the world with joy

Mary and Joe, traveled to and fro

To welcome their new baby boy

An angel came down, to see what was around

Then proclaimed to the world with joy

Mary Had A Little Boy

(Tune of "Mary Had A Little Lamb")

Mary had a little boy
Who's born on Christmas day
He is God's only son
Who took our sins away

Mary had a little boy
Who's born on Christmas day
He is God's only son
Who took our sins away

Three Wisemen
(Tune of "Three Blind Mice")

Three wisemen, three wisemen

See how they roam, see how they roam

They came to see their newborn king

To pay him homage with gifts to bring

Hark the herald angels sing

For three wisemen

It's Sleeting, It's Snowing

(Tune of "It's Raining, It's Pouring")

It's sleeting, it's snowing

Are schools closed this morning?

I stayed in bed

For this I dread

I lie awake not knowing

It's sleeting, it's snowing

Are schools closed this morning?

I stayed in bed

For this I dread

I lie awake not knowing

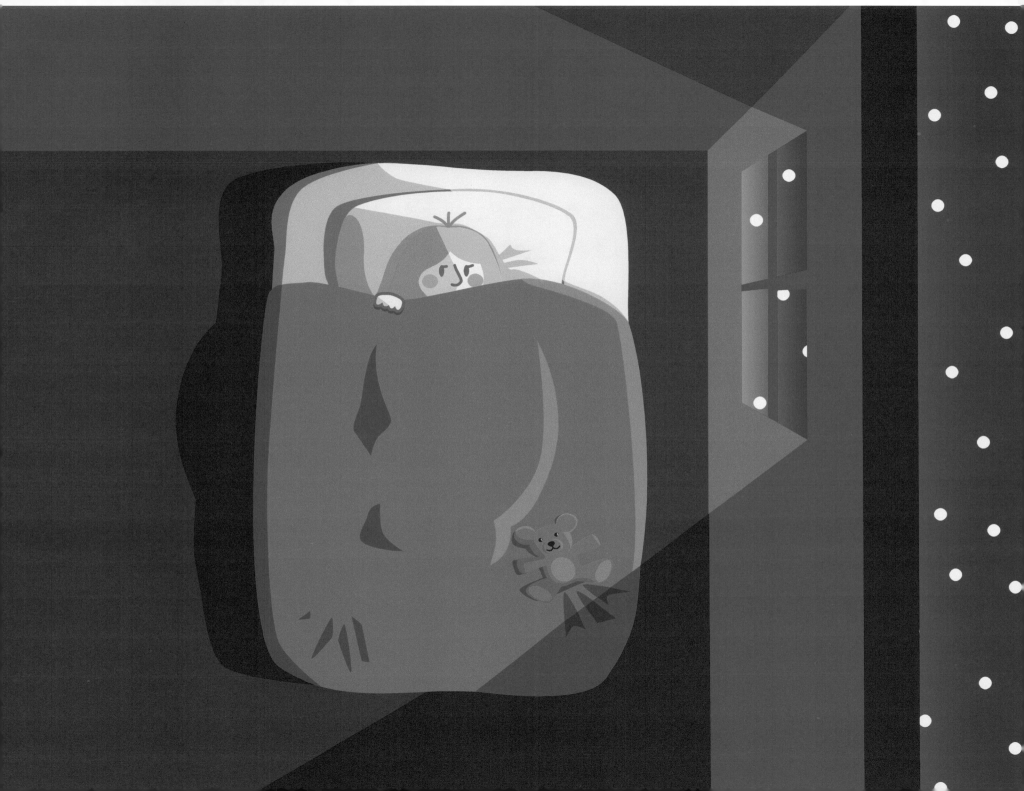

Ryan Markowitz

Ryan was born and raised in the suburbs of Philadelphia. Ever since he was a child he always loved being creative. Ryan was encouraged by his parents and teachers at an early age to pursue being an artist. He graduated with a bachelors in graphic design and continued to pursue his creative style. Ryan contributes his passion for art and creativity to his Lord and savior, Jesus Christ. Whom he believes from the very beginning had planned for him to be an artist and to illustrate this book. His style in this book is that of vibrant colors, simplistic shapes, and pockets of focused detail. Ryan's hope for this book is to bring joy to those who read it and to promote the reason for Christmas to kids.

Barry Weidner

Barry was born in Allentown, PA, and raised in the suburbs of Philadelphia. After going away to college in Washington D.C., he decided to return to his roots where he currently resides with his wife Jocelyn and three children, Emma, Brady, and Samuel. Barry enjoyed playing multiple sports growing up and played collegiate soccer. He grew up a huge Philly sports fan, especially the Phillies and Eagles. Barry has an expansive love of music, specifically rock & roll. His true passion is in health and fitness. He was able to turn that passion into a career when he started his own gym business with Jocelyn in 2007. During the Covid pandemic while the gym was shut down, Barry found creative writing to be an artistic outlet and looks forward to writing more books in the years to come.

Chelsea Stanell

Chelsea is thrilled to be a part of "This Snowman" and hopes that you enjoy singing along with her during your adventures through the book. She is a professional musician and a high school music teacher in the Philadelphia area. She is a dog mom to Lala and as of June 2022, she now is a wife to her husband Tony. Chelsea has always had a passion for music, singing, and especially for celebrating Christmas with loved ones! She belongs to Barry & Jocelyn's gym and was overjoyed to be asked to be a part of "This Snowman." May your days be merry and bright and all of your singing delight!

Printed in the USA
CPSIA information can be obtained
at www.ICGtesting.com
JSHW040335100923
48147JS00003B/5